Published by Ladybird Books Ltd.
A Penguin Company. Penguin Books, 80 Strand, London, WC2R 0RL, UK

ISBN: 9781409300113

2 4 6 8 10 9 7 5 3 1

Printed in Slovakia

STAR THE CLONE WARS WARS

FRONT ROW SEAT

A long time ago, in a galaxy far, far away....

The Republic is at war! Supreme Chancellor Palpatine has committed thousands of troops to the war against Count Dooku's Separatist Alliance. As planets choose sides, the galaxy is divided and only the valiant efforts of Republic clone troopers and their Jedi generals hold the fracturing Republic from tearing apart.

ANAKIN SKYWALKER AND OBI-WAN KENOBI HAVE SCORED A RARE VICTORY FOR THE REPUBLIC ON THE PLANET CHRISTOPHSIS. A NEW PADAWAN LEARNER ARRIVES IN TIME TO AID THE JEDI, BUT SHE'S NOT TO STUDY UNDER OBI-WAN AS EXPECTED, BUT UNDER ANAKIN, WHO SWORE HE'D NEVER TAKE AN APPRENTICE.

AS WAR SPREADS CHAOS ACROSS THE GALAXY, CRIME LORD JABBA THE HUTT'S SON IS KIDNAPPED. IN ORDER TO GAIN SAFE PASSAGE THROUGH THE HUTT'S SYSTEMS, THE JEDI HAVE AGREED TO FIND AND RESCUE JABBA'S SON.

ON TATOOINE, OBI-WAN CONCLUDES HIS MEETING WITH THE FEARED JABBA THE HUTT . . .

ALL RIGHT ANAKIN, HERE'S THE STORY.

. . . AND IMMEDIATELY CONTACTS ANAKIN AND HIS NEW PADAWAN, AHSOKA TANO, TO FILL THEM IN ON THE DETAILS OF ROTTA THE HUTTLET'S KIDNAPPING.

JABBA HAS GIVEN US ONLY ONE PLANETARY ROTATION TO GET HIS SON BACK HOME TO TATOOINE SAFE AND SOUND.

IT WON'T TAKE US THAT LONG, MASTER.

WE HAVE NO IDEA WHO IS HOLDING JABBA'S SON. WHEN I'VE FINISHED NEGOTIATIONS WITH HIM, I WILL JOIN YOU.

ANAKIN AND AHSOKA'S INVESTIGATION LEADS THEM TO PLANET TETH . . .

I SENSE OUR KIDNAPPED HUTT IS IN HERE.

. . . WHERE THEY FIND ROTTA THE HUTTLET IN A DUNGEON.

ROTTA IS SICK, CRYING AND MISSES HIS FATHER.

HE'S JUST A BABY. THIS WILL MAKE OUR JOB A LOT EASIER. HE'S SO CUTE!

BACK ON TATOOINE, JABBA RECEIVES AN OMINOUS GUEST.

OH GREAT JABBA THE HUTT, I HAVE NEWS OF YOUR SON. I HAVE DISCOVERED IT IS THE JEDI WHO HAVE KIDNAPPED HIM.

DOOKU SPREADS LIES IN THE HOPE OF GAINING JABBA AS A SEPARATIST ALLY.

DOOKU WANA JEEMEEESHKA!

HOW HAVE YOU COME BY THIS INFORMATION?

TRANSLATOR DROID!

I HAVE MY WAYS. MORE IMPORTANTLY, MIGHTY JABBA, I BRING A WARNING. THE JEDI ARE PLANNING TO DESTROY YOU!

UHHH WOOONKA MEE CEESKOH!

THE MOST WISE JABBA DEMANDS PROOF!

AND HE SHALL HAVE IT!

ANAKIN, DID YOU LOCATE JABBA'S SON?

OUTSIDE THE CASTLE ON PLANET TETH, ANAKIN AND OBI-WAN ARE BEGINNING TO UNRAVEL THE MYSTERIOUS KIDNAPPING OF THE HUTTLET.

WE HAVE HIM, BUT IT LOOKS LIKE THE SEPARATISTS ARE BEHIND HIS ABDUCTION. THIS SMELLS LIKE COUNT DOOKU TO ME.

I'LL BET DOOKU IS USING US TO GET JABBA TO JOIN THE SEPARATISTS.

I'M NOT SURE WE CAN GET HIM BACK TO TATOOINE ALIVE, MASTER. THIS WHOLE RESCUE MAY BACKFIRE ON US. I STILL DON'T THINK DEALING WITH THE HUTTS IS A GOOD IDEA.

I'LL HAVE TO CALL YOU BACK, MASTER.

DEFENSIVE POSITIONS!

WE'RE UNDER ATTACK! WE COULD USE A LITTLE HELP HERE, IF YOU HAVE THE TIME.

MASTER SKYWALKER, I'VE BEEN SO LOOKING FORWARD TO ANOTHER ENCOUNTER WITH YOU. I SEE YOU'VE FOUND YOURSELF A NEW PET.

DOOKU'S ASSASSIN, ASAJJ VENTRESS, FINDS THE JEDI AS THEY TRY TO RESCUE ROTTA.

I'M NO PET!

CAREFUL, SHE BITES!

JUST GIVE ME THE HUTT, SKYWALKER! I WILL FINISH YOU FIRST, SO YOU WON'T HAVE TO WATCH YOUR SILLY YOUNGLING DIE.

SECRETLY, R2-D2 GLIDES OVER TO ONE OF THE CASTLE'S ELECTRONIC INSTRUMENT PANELS THAT CONTROLS THE GRATE THAT EVERYONE IS STANDING ON.

THE GRATE OPENS, SENDING THE JEDI, VENTRESS AND HER BATTLE DROIDS PLUMMETING TO UNKNOWN LEVELS BELOW THEM.

THE LITTLE DROID EVEN KNOCKS THE LAST OF THE BATTLE DROIDS OVER THE EDGE.

THIS IS IT! SCRAP 'EM!

OUTSIDE THE CASTLE, THE CLONE TROOPERS ARE TRYING DESPERATELY TO HOLD OFF THE BATTLE DROIDS' ADVANCING FORCES.

NO MATTER HOW HARD THEY FIGHT, THERE ARE JUST TOO MANY BATTLE DROIDS.

WE'VE GOT YOU OUTNUMBERED!

SURRENDER, REPUBLIC DOGS!

EVENTUALLY, THE CLONE TROOPERS ARE SURROUNDED.

SUDDENLY, OBI-WAN ARRIVES WITH MUCH NEEDED REINFORCEMENTS.

WHERE'S SKYWALKER?

BEST GUESS SAYS HE'S STILL IN THE CASTLE, SIR.

KEEP THE DROIDS OCCUPIED. I'LL GO FIND HIM.

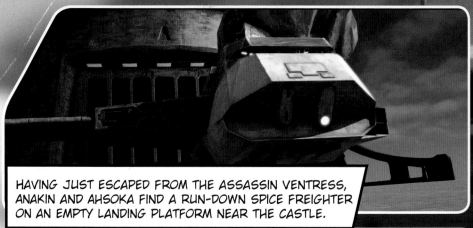

HAVING JUST ESCAPED FROM THE ASSASSIN VENTRESS,
ANAKIN AND AHSOKA FIND A RUN-DOWN SPICE FREIGHTER
ON AN EMPTY LANDING PLATFORM NEAR THE CASTLE.

THE JEDI PREPARE TO TAKE OFF AND HEAD
TOWARDS JABBA'S PALACE ON TATOOINE . . .

. . . BUT THE ENGINES FAIL TO IGNITE.

NOW LET'S GET STINKY
OUTTA HERE. UH, IF WE
CAN!

ARTOO, SEE IF YOU CAN SPARK THE IGNITION COUPLERS.

ONCE AGAIN, R2-D2 SAVES THE DAY.

THE ENGINES ROAR TO LIFE AND THE SPICE FREIGHTER *TWILIGHT* TAKES OFF.

CAPTAIN REX, THIS IS GENERAL SKYWALKER.

AS THE *TWILIGHT* LEAVES PLANET TETH, ANAKIN CONTACTS CAPTAIN REX WITH SOME BAD NEWS.

YES, GENERAL.

WE'RE NOT GOING TO BE ABLE TO HELP YOU.

DON'T WORRY ABOUT US, GENERAL. WE'LL BE ALL RIGHT!

AS ANAKIN SIGNS OFF, ANOTHER WAVE OF BATTLE
DROID FORCES ATTACK THE REMAINING CLONES.

THE CLONES FEROCIOUSLY FIGHT BACK . . .

. . . AND HOPE THERE ARE ENOUGH CLONE
TROOPERS LEFT TO WIN THIS BATTLE.

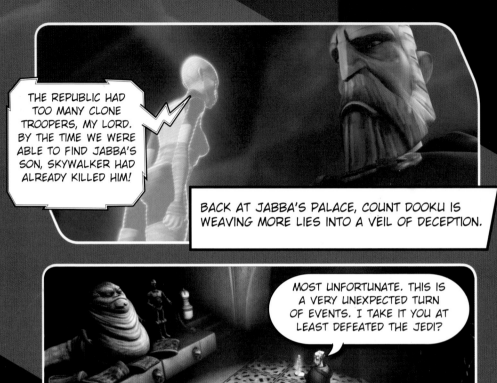

THE REPUBLIC HAD TOO MANY CLONE TROOPERS, MY LORD. BY THE TIME WE WERE ABLE TO FIND JABBA'S SON, SKYWALKER HAD ALREADY KILLED HIM!

BACK AT JABBA'S PALACE, COUNT DOOKU IS WEAVING MORE LIES INTO A VEIL OF DECEPTION.

MOST UNFORTUNATE. THIS IS A VERY UNEXPECTED TURN OF EVENTS. I TAKE IT YOU AT LEAST DEFEATED THE JEDI?

NO, MASTER! THE JEDI ESCAPED AND ARE HEADED TO TATOOINE.

I'M SURE YOU DID THE BEST YOU COULD. WE WILL DISCUSS YOUR FAILURE LATER.

GLORIOUS JABBA DEMANDS TO KNOW WHY THE JEDI WOULD DARE COME TO TATOOINE.

AH! YAPOTA JEDI AMA TATOOINE?

TO KILL YOU, JABBA.

THE JEDI PLOT IS QUITE CLEAR NOW. THEY ONLY PROMISED TO RESCUE YOUR SON TO WIN YOUR TRUST. NOW SKYWALKER IS COMING HERE TO FINISH HIS TRUE MISSION, TO WIPE OUT THE ENTIRE HUTT CLAN.

ON CORUSCANT, YODA AND CHANCELLOR PALPATINE RECEIVE A SITUATION REPORT FROM OBI-WAN.

ANAKIN HAS REACHED TATOOINE WITH THE HUTTLET, MASTER, BUT HE'S STILL IN GRAVE DANGER. SEPARATIST TROOPS ARE DESPERATE TO INTERCEPT HIM. I THINK THIS WHOLE PLOT WAS ENGINEERED BY DOOKU TO CONVINCE JABBA WE KIDNAPPED HIS SON.

IF BELIEVE THIS THE HUTTS DO, ENDED WILL OUR CHANCE OF A TREATY WITH THEM BE. JOIN DOOKU AND THE SEPARATISTS, JABBA WILL.

THAT WOULD BE A DISASTER. WE MUST HAVE THIS ALLIANCE WITH THE HUTTS IF WE ARE TO WIN THE WAR IN THE OUTER RIM.

IN SKYWALKER IS THE REPUBLIC'S ONLY HOPE. RETURN JABBA'S SON, HE MUST!

ANAKIN'S EXPERIENCE WITH THE HUTTS SHOULD HELP. HE'LL COME THROUGH!

AS SENATOR AMIDALA IS ESCORTED OUT OF ZIRO'S PALACE, SHE BECOMES CONVINCED THAT SHE NEEDS TO TALK TO ZIRO AGAIN AND GIVES HER GUARD THE SLIP.

SHE RETURNS TO THE THRONE ROOM TO FIND ZIRO COMMUNICATING WITH A SINISTER FIGURE.

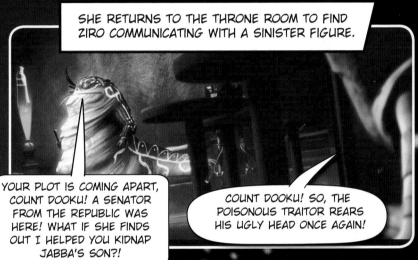

YOUR PLOT IS COMING APART, COUNT DOOKU! A SENATOR FROM THE REPUBLIC WAS HERE! WHAT IF SHE FINDS OUT I HELPED YOU KIDNAP JABBA'S SON?!

COUNT DOOKU! SO, THE POISONOUS TRAITOR REARS HIS UGLY HEAD ONCE AGAIN!

I'M EQUALLY DELIGHTED TO REMAKE YOUR ACQUAINTANCE, SENATOR . . . AMIDALA, ISN'T IT?

THE SENATOR IS NOT AS QUIET AS SHE HOPED AND IS NOTICED BY THE TWO CONSPIRATORS.

29

ON TATOOINE, DOOKU LEAVES JABBA'S PALACE AND ATTACKS ANAKIN AND THE HUTTLET...

YOUR TRAINING HAS COME A LONG WAY, BOY. THIS WAS YOUR HOME PLANET, WASN'T IT? I SENSE STRONG FEELINGS. FEELINGS OF PAIN, LOSS.

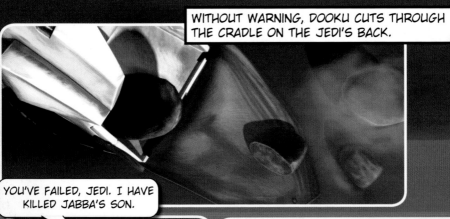

WITHOUT WARNING, DOOKU CUTS THROUGH THE CRADLE ON THE JEDI'S BACK.

YOU'VE FAILED, JEDI. I HAVE KILLED JABBA'S SON.

YOU'VE FALLEN FOR MY LITTLE TRICK, COUNT. IT'S NOTHING BUT ROCKS. THE HUTTLET IS WITH MY PADAWAN, SAFE AT JABBA'S PALACE.

LOOK, I HAVE A MESSAGE FROM YOUR PADAWAN. AFTER MY DROIDS KILL JABBA'S SON, THEY WILL DELIVER YOUR PADAWAN TO HIM. I CAN'T IMAGINE HE WILL BE MERCIFUL.

KNOWING DOOKU SPEAKS THE TRUTH AND FEARING FOR HIS PADAWAN'S LIFE, ANAKIN FLEES HIS FIGHT WITH THE COUNT RATHER THAN WASTE ANY MORE TIME.

YOU TRIED TO CALL FOR HELP. SENATOR, I BELIEVE THAT YOU ARE TOO DANGEROUS TO BE KEPT ALIVE!

BACK ON CORUSCANT, SENATOR AMIDALA IS BROUGHT BEFORE ZIRO.

KILLING A GALACTIC SENATOR, HERE ON CORUSCANT? ARE YOU OUT OF YOUR MIND?

I HAVE POWERFUL FRIENDS IN THE SENATE! I'M NOT AFRAID OF...

HUH?! WHAT IS THAT?!

SUDDENLY, A CADRE OF CLONE TROOPERS STORM ZIRO'S PALACE.

RUN FOR IT!!

STOP, ZIRO! STOP RIGHT WHERE YOU ARE!

AT JABBA'S PALACE . . .

WHAT HAVE YOU DONE WITH MY PADAWAN?!

AHHH! SKYWALKER KILLYE!

YOU CAME HERE TO KILL JABBA!

STOP!

ALL OF A SUDDEN, AHSOKA BURSTS INTO THE THRONE ROOM.

MOST PATIENT JABBA, YOUR SON HAS ARRIVED. ALIVE AND WELL.

ROTTA, ME PEEDUNKEE?

PEEDUNKEE MUFKIN!

HA HA HA! KOOTU BARGON TAGWA!

JABBA AGREES. A TREATY IS IN ORDER.

IT IS UNFORTUNATE, MASTER. THE JEDI ARMIES WILL NOW HAVE THEIR SUPPLY ROUTES TO THE OUTER RIM.

OUR FIGHT HAS BECOME FAR MORE DIFFICULT.

ALLOW THE JEDI THEIR SMALL VICTORY, MY FRIEND, FOR THE ENGINES OF THIS WAR TURN IN OUR FAVOUR.

THE END.